Our Journey So Far . . .

Everything about this project has been a joyous adventure in collaboration.

The story was penned at the behest of friends. Caroline asked for a poem about a campervan and many others proposed what to cram into it. The 'Hunk of Tin' folk song proved the perfect 'vehicle' and Honk! Honk! Rattle! Rattle! was born.

It soon became part of my storytelling repertoire and an instant hit with the crowds of children who attend the Wigtown Book Festival.

Shortly after, I served as a Reader in Residence for Dumfries and Galloway Libraries. This post was funded by the Scottish Book Trust, whose wonderful purpose it is to promote literature, reading, and writing.

As storytelling was at the heart of my role, it seemed a fitting legacy to leave the region (and far beyond) with a picture book.

Cue the entrance of the clearly magnificent and anarchic Mike Abel, illustrator, also a Wigtownshire dweller. Our collaboration has been an inexpressible honour for me. He has taken my story and made it ours, creating a cast of characters that have caused me to laugh out loud throughout our own journey to bring this book to you.

We have so many people to thank, particularly those nearest and dearest to us, Eric, Jude and Emma Louise.

Special thanks to Jayne and Shalla of Curly Tale Books Ltd. for their advice, support and tea and to Shirley Barrass of Hippidippies Gifts and Gallery for many hugs.

Huge thanks to Anne Rinaldi (my library partner), our Kickstart backers, local biz sponsors and media mates who got Honk! Honk! Rattle! Rattle! to the top of the FUNdraising hill, cheering for us along the way. You will find many of our supporters named inside.

Big shout out also for the Scottish Storytelling Centre whose goal it is to support the tradition of oral storytelling and tellers. I am so proud to be among you.

Like all picture books, Mike and I hope that Honk! Honk! Rattle! Rattle! will be a joyous tool of togetherness, a shared tale-telling experience that will strengthen bonds and build literacy skills.

May your journeys together be filled with a sense of humour and an abundance of love.

Renita

Thanks to our many **KICKSTARTER** backers/local sponsors, supporters and media mates who helped to make this book possible.

Honk! Honk! Rattle! Rattle! First Print

ISBN 978-0-9574323-9-0

Published by J&B Print
Produced by Tell Together Tales www.telltogethertales.com

Note: The repeated refrain only of this original derivative work is in the public domain and is free of known restrictions under copyright law, including all related and neighbouring rights. You may recognise it from the 'Hunk of Tin' folk song which has been enjoyed by successive silly singing generations. Its origins remain unknown.

Printed in the UK by J&B Print, 32A Albert Street, Newton Stewart, DG8 6EJ

With thanks for your continued sharing and media support

Alive Radio 107.3 fm

Dumfries and Galloway Libraries

Dumfries and Galloway Life Magazine

Dumfries and Galloway! What's Going On?

Our Wigtownshire Magazine

Stranraer Free Press

The Galloway Gazette

Wigtown Festival Company

Honk! Honk! Rattle! Rattle!

...a comic camping caper with a crew of quirky critters and kids in a campervan.

Renita Boyle

Mike Abel

Tell Together Tales

Find Hammy Hamster in every picture

We've got a kite to fly and a boat to sail,
a fishing pole and a mop and pail,
a flute to toot and an old banjo,
a basket full of food and a chef to go!

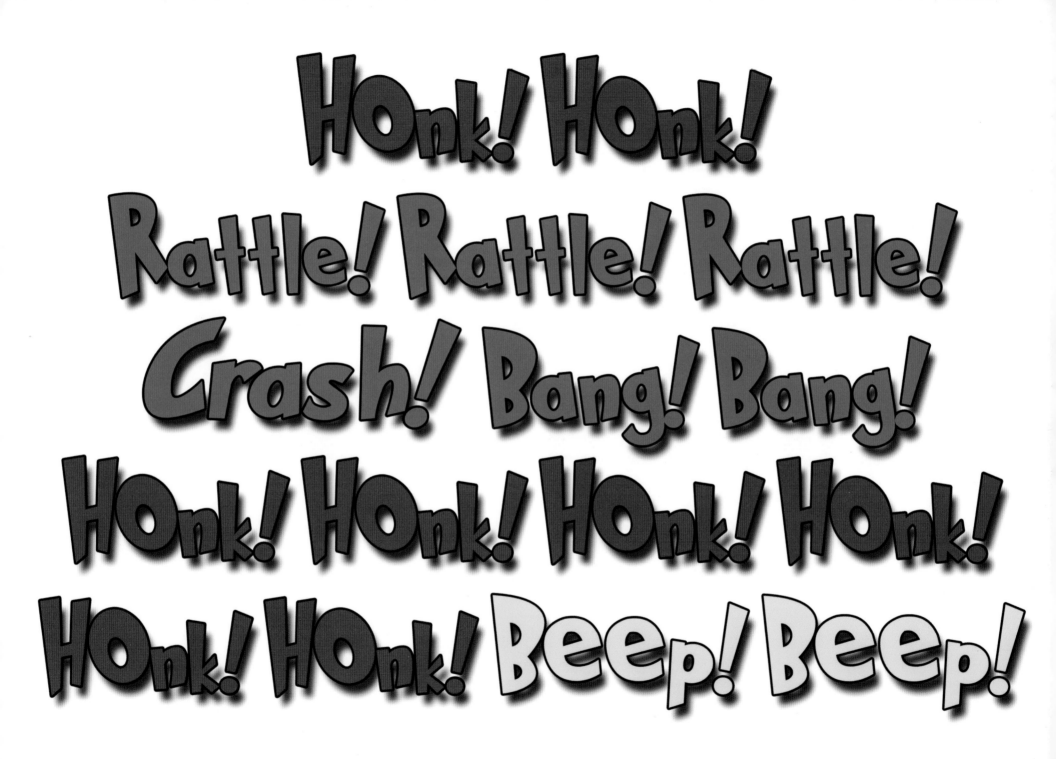

We've got sticky tape and a first aid kit,

a needle and thread and wool to knit,
a long clothes line and loads of pegs,
a wonky chair with wobbly legs.

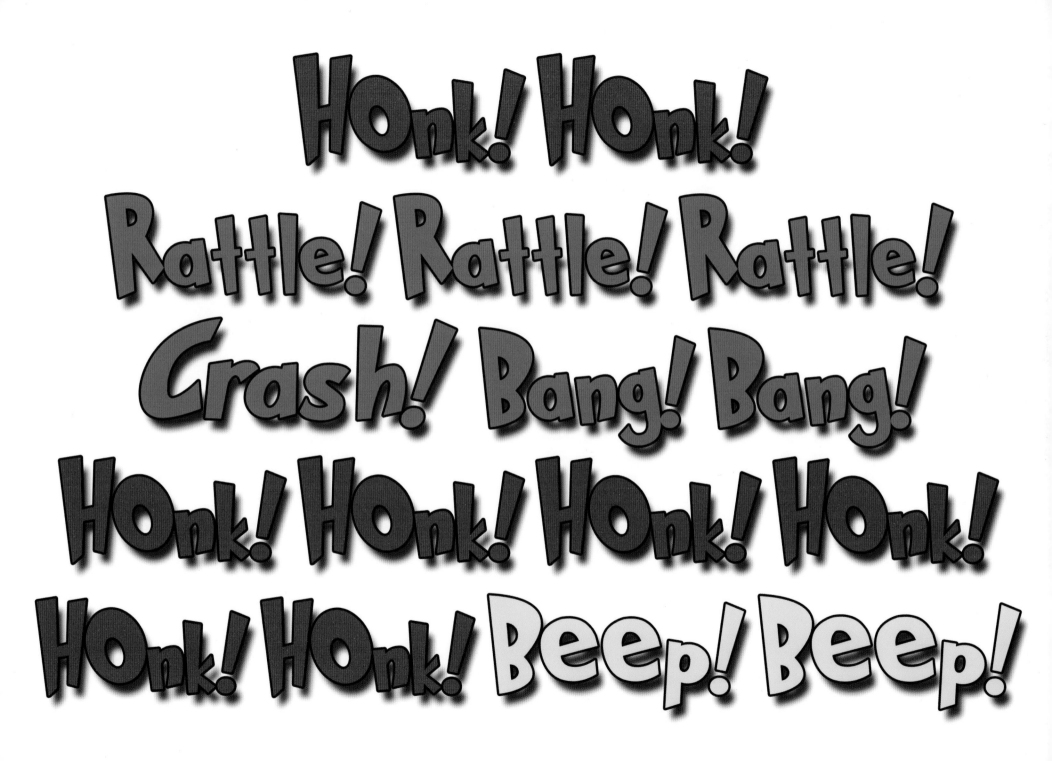

There's a small bandana and a big balloon, glitter and glue and a dog that moos,

a cat that vrooms and
a motor that purrs,
a horse that quacks
and a spoon to stir.

There's a big bath tub and a mountain bike,
boots and a map for a hill-top hike,
A stack of books and our favourite tunes,
wood for a fire under stars and moon.

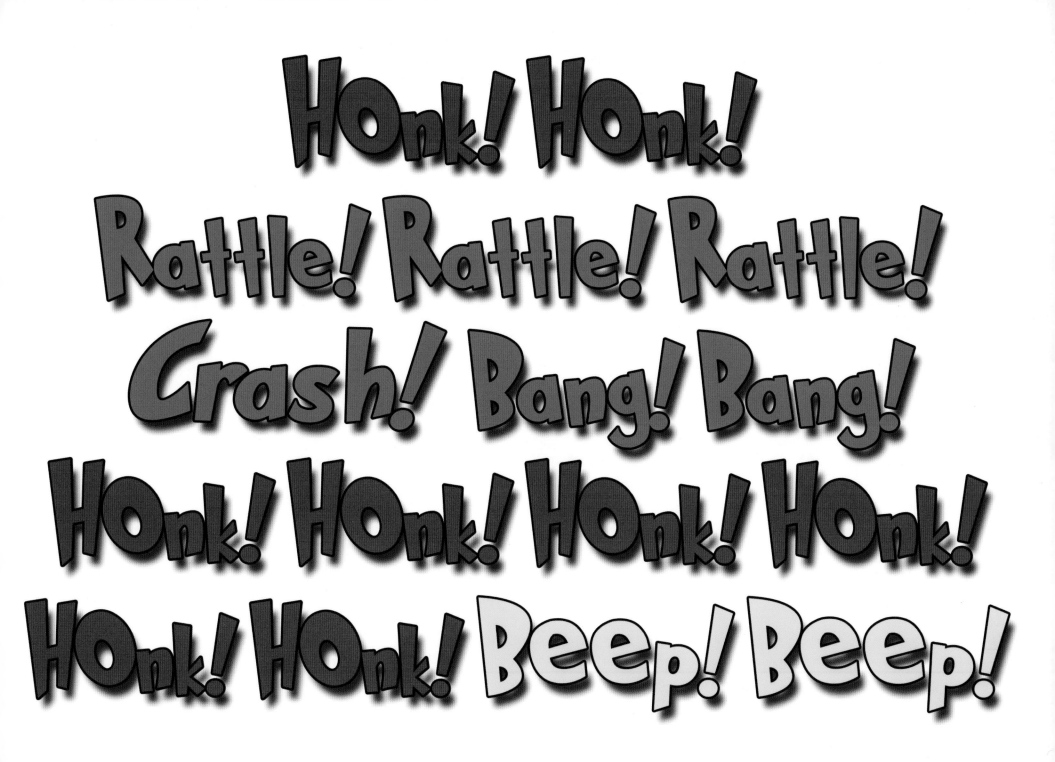

Got wellies, brollies, mitts and hats,
sunblock, goggles, balls and a bat,

SHOWERS →

← CAMP

a mouse that squeaks and tyres that squeal,
and an itty bitty hamster at the wheel.

Got pots and pans and all of their lids,
a bunch of flowers and a batch of kids,

Ten Things to Know About Renita

• I am a tale-telling, tongue-twisting troubadour and KidLit poet
• I have been telling stories and singing silly songs for as long as I can remember
• I can play the bagpipe with my nose and have taught thousands of children to do the same (ask me sometime!)
• I am very good friends with the three funky little pigs, the silliest man in the world and a head banging rockstar frog
• I head butt grumpy trolls into the river and make amazing imaginary peanut butter and jelly sandwiches
• I have never been able to figure out why the old woman swallowed a fly (have you?)
• I once played the back end of an elephant in a skit and told stories to a truly captive audience in a broken lift (elevator)
• I grew up in America but have lived in Scotland for over 31 years; I now live in Wigtown, Scotland's National Book Town
• I LOVE! LOVE! LOVE! Messy Church and my Messy Church peeps
• But not as much as I love my hubby Eric; my son Jude; and my dog, Bonnie Belle Boyle

Find me: www.renitaboyle.com

Ten Things to Know About Mike

• I am 41 and have loved drawing since I was a child
• I believe that imagination is the best gift anyone can have
• I take things from life and think of other ways it can be used
• I couldn't imagine a day without drawing
• I take most of my inspiration from daydreaming
• I have a degree in illustration, but have always loved doing things my own way; messing about with lots of mediums and learning from my mistakes
• I love everything from mice to monsters
• I also love The Muppets® and Calvin and Hobbs®
• I grew up in Yorkshire but now live in Dumfries & Galloway with my wife Emma Louise and our cat Pookie
• This is my first children's picture book and I hope you love it!

Find me: fb.me/IllustratorMikeAbel

Hippidippies Gifts & Gallery

Emma Louise Dance Club

Glaisnock Café

Unit 3 Art Gallery

The Old Bank Bookshop

Community Shop

Bayview Bistro

Café Rendezvous

Andrew Plunkett Steel Buildings

Wigtown Motor Company

Byre Books

Briars Engravers

Wigtown Festival Company

Scads

Reading Lasses

The Open Book

The Kist

Craigard Gallery

Curly Tale Books

The Bookshop

Bladnoch Inn

Hair Do's

Historic Newspapers

Barclays Garage

Peter Thomson & Son Ltd

Hillcrest House Hotel

The Bookend Studio

All Sorts

Traditions

Craft Burgers & Beer

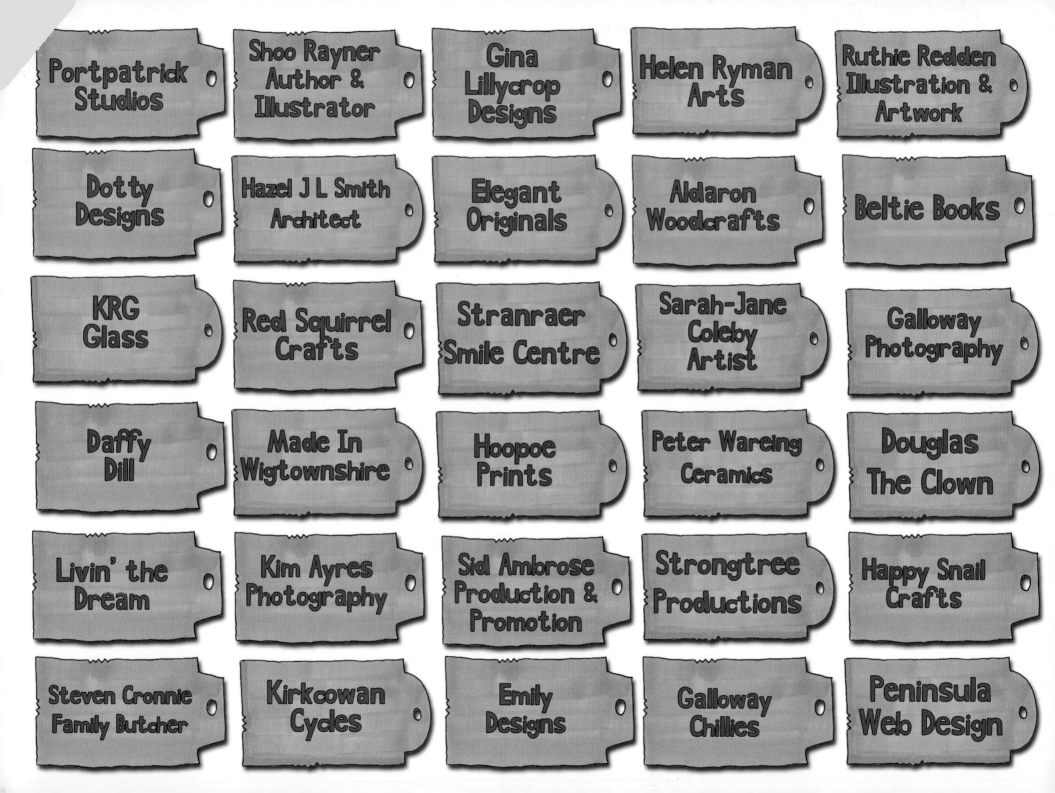

Portpatrick Studios

Shoo Rayner Author & Illustrator

Gina Lillycrop Designs

Helen Ryman Arts

Ruthie Redden Illustration & Artwork

Dotty Designs

Hazel J L Smith Architect

Elegant Originals

Aldaron Woodcrafts

Beltie Books

KRG Glass

Red Squirrel Crafts

Stranraer Smile Centre

Sarah-Jane Coleby Artist

Galloway Photography

Daffy Dill

Made In Wigtownshire

Hoopoe Prints

Peter Wareing Ceramics

Douglas The Clown

Livin' the Dream

Kim Ayres Photography

Sid Ambrose Production & Promotion

Strongtree Productions

Happy Snail Crafts

Steven Cronnie Family Butcher

Kirkcowan Cycles

Emily Designs

Galloway Chillies

Peninsula Web Design